S0-AWG-738

Animals Birds & Fishes on COINS

*TOPICAL
COIN LIBRARY*

By Gunther Schon
Assisted by A.V. Ziegesar

STERLING PUBLISHING CO., INC.   NEW YORK

Oak Tree Press Co., Ltd.
Distributed by WARD LOCK, Ltd., London & Sydney

COIN AND STAMP BOOKS

Copyright © 1971 by
President Coin Corporation
4 Warwick Place, Port Washington, New York 11050
Distributed to the Book Trade by
Sterling Publishing Co., Inc.
419 Park Avenue South, New York, N.Y. 10016
British edition published by Oak Tree Press Co., Ltd.
Distributed in Great Britain and the Commonwealth by
Ward Lock, Ltd., 116 Baker Street, London W1
Adapted from "Tiermotiv Katalog"
© 1970 by Ernst Battenberg Verlag, Munich, Germany
Manufactured in the United States of America
All rights reserved
Library of Congress Catalog Card No.: 79-126854
ISBN 0-8069-6026-6   UK 7061 2266 6
6027-4

Contents

A parade of animals and birds encircles the obverse of this 1957 5 rupee coin issued in Ceylon to celebrate the 2,500th anniversary of Buddhism.

About This Book

When you start collecting coins by the pictures on the obverse and reverse, you will find such unusual animals, birds and fishes as the aardvark, hornbill, titmouse, badger, sow and piglets, hen and chicks, kangaroo and emu, bongafish and angelfish. Each of these subjects has been chosen for a reason, and learning the stories behind the coins often leads to a whole new appreciation of coins. Australia, for example, boasts many animals that are found only on that continent and the Australian government has pictured a different one on each denomination coin. Eagles and lions, on the other hand, have been featured prominently on the coins of many nations. These interesting topical coins are fun to collect and are worth examining and displaying, as the pictures and valuations in this book show. This catalogue lists only the modern coins of the world which portray members of the animal family and does not include coins that picture mythical creatures such as dragons.

The serious numismatist will be more concerned with the condition of his coins than with the pictures on their faces, but the beginning collector, who is not acquainted with the finer points of numismatics, will certainly find pictures more fascinating than mint marks, and the animal kingdom more entertaining than a milled edge or a quantities-issued table. A real zoo springs from the pages of this book or, better still, from a collection of the coins themselves. Perhaps reading this book will lead on to a life-long interest in coins, and hopefully a deeper appreciation for the creatures that share our globe.

Land Animals

AARDVARK

These unusual animals which can grow to a length of five feet, wobble along on tall, thick legs. Their deep-set, narrow heads are topped with a pair of long, donkey ears.

1. *Zambia*, 1 Ngwee (Br) 1968. Head of President Kuanda $ .25

ANTEATER (SPINY)

Spiny anteaters are native to the dry country of Australia and New Guinea. Covered with a mixture of coarse hair and long quills, these foot-long mammals use their claws, tapering snouts and long tongues to feed on ants.

1. *Australia*, 5 Cents (CN) 1966. Draped bust of Queen Elizabeth II   .20

* *Indicates coin or coins illustrated*

ANTELOPE

Especially abundant in Africa, antelopes are cud-chewing mammals of slender, graceful build. They are distinguished by their up-swept horns. Antelopes generally travel in small herds, wandering great distances in search of water.

*1. *Cameroon* (French colony), 2 Francs (Al) 1948. Bust of Republic   .50
2. 1 Franc (Al) 1948   .35

*3. *Cameroon* (unified coinage with French Equatorial Africa), 25 Francs (Al-Br) 1958, 59. Value in wreath   .75
4. 10 Francs (Al-Br) 1958   .50
5. 5 Francs (Al-Br) 1958   .35
6. *Cameroon* (independent state), 50 Francs (Al-Br) 1960   1.50
7. 100 Francs (N) 1966. Value in circle   2.00

1. *French Equatorial Africa*, 2 Francs (Al) 1948. .50
   (Same type as Cameroon #1)
2. 1 Franc (Al) 1948 .25
   (See Cameroon No. 3-5)

*1. *Equatorial African States*, 50 Francs (CN) 1961.
   Value in wreath 2.00
2. 25 Francs (Al-Br) 1962– .75
3. 10 Francs (Al-Br) 1961– .50
4. 5 Francs (Al-Br) 1961– .35
5. 100 Francs (N) 1966. Value in circle 1.50

*1. *French Somaliland*, 5 Francs (Al) 1948–65. Bust
   of Republic .60
2. 2 Francs (Al) 1948–65 .35
3. 1 Franc (Al) 1949, 59 .25

1. *French West Africa*, 2 Francs (Al) 1948–55. Bust
   of Republic .50
2. 1 Franc (Al) 1948–55 .20
*3. 25 Francs (Al-Br) 1956. Head of Republic 1.50
4. 10 Francs (Al-Br) 1956 1.00
5. 5 Francs (Al-Br) 1956 .75

6. *French West Africa* (Unified coinage with Togo),
   25 Francs (Al-Br) 1957 1.00
*7. 10 Francs (Al-Br) 1957. Native mask .65

1. *Rhodesia-Nyasaland*, 1 Shilling (CN) 1955–57.
   Head of Queen Elizabeth II .75
*2. 2½ Shillings—25 Cents (CN) 1964 2.50

*1. *Southern Rhodesia*, 2 Shillings (S) 1932–36.
   Crowned bust of King George V 5.00
2. 2 Shillings (S) 1937–46; (CN) 1947–52. Crowned
   head of King George VI 2.25
3. 2 Shillings (CN) 1954. Head of Queen Elizabeth II 6.50

1. *Togo*, 2 Francs (Al) 1948. Bust of Republic 2.00
*2. 1 Franc (Al) 1948 1.00
3. 5 Francs (Al-Br) 1956. Head of Republic. (See
   French West Africa #6 and #7) 2.00

*1. *Uganda*, 2 Shillings (CN) 1966. Mountains and
   crane   .75
2. 1 Shilling (CN) 1966   .45
3. 50 Cents (CN) 1966   .30

ANTELOPE (ORIBI BUCK)

Oribi antelopes are found only in eastern
Africa. Standing about 24 inches at the
shoulder, oribis are a tawny yellow color with
white underneath. Their curved, ringed horns,
which only the males have, grow to five inches.

*1. *Zambia*, 2 Shillings (CN) 1964. Coat-of-arms   1.50
2. 2 Shillings (CN) 1966. Head of President Kuanda   1.50
3. 20 Ngwee (CN) 1968   1.25

ANTELOPE (WILDEBEEST)

Also called gnu, wildebeest antelopes range
through central Africa. Rather large, with ox-
like heads, they have smooth horns that curve
downward, outward and then up. They have
short manes and flowing horse-like tails.

1. *South Africa*, 2 Cents (Br) 1965. Bust of Jan van
   Riebeeck, SOUTH AFRICA   .15
*2. 2 Cents (Br) 1965. Type of #1 but SUID AFRIKA   .15
3. 2 Cents (Br) 1968. Head of Charles Swart,
   SOUTH AFRICA   .15
4. 2 Cents (Br) 1968, SUID AFRIKA   .15

BADGER

American badgers, the emblem of Wisconsin, the "Badger State," are found from
southern Canada to Mexico, mainly in the
plains areas. Nocturnal animals, they feed on
roots, young birds and mammals.

1. *United States*, 50 Cents (S) 1936. Wisconsin
   Territorial Centennial   35.00

BEAR (GRIZZLY)

Although grizzly bears once roamed
throughout western North America, the
species now has been almost exterminated. A
few can be seen in protected areas, especially
in Yellowstone National Park. Their food is
game, fish and berries. Some grizzly bears have
been known to weigh more than 1,000 pounds.

7

The emblem of California, the grizzly has been featured on coins related to that state.

1. *United States*, 50 Cents (S) 1925. California Diamond Jubilee   20.00

2. 50 Cents (S) 1935, 36. California Pacific Exposition   25.00

3. 50 Cents (S) 1936. San Francisco-Oakland Bay Bridge   30.00

BEAR (POLAR)

Native to the Arctic areas, the white polar bear is a powerful swimmer and can stay under water for two minutes. During the winter months, polar bears hibernate in deep snow tunnels.

*1. *Greenland*, 5 Kroner (Al-Br) 1944. Arms   5.00
2. 1 Krone (Al-Br) 1926–57   1.50

3. 1 Krone (Al-Br) 1957; (CN) 1960–64. Value in wreath   1.50

BEAVER

Distinguished by their flat, hairless tails, beavers live in small streams where they build strong dams to deepen the water. They then build lodges with the entrance below the surface.

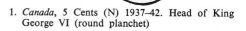

1. *Canada*, 5 Cents (N) 1937–42. Head of King George VI (round planchet)   .60

2. 5 Cents (Tombac) 1942 (12-sided planchet)   2.00
3. 5 Cents (N) 1946–50; (St) 1951–52   .45
4. 5 Cents (N) 1953–62. Head of Queen Elizabeth II
   (12-sided planchet)   .15
5. 5 Cents (N) 1963 (round planchet)   .15
6. 5 Cents (N) 1965– . Draped bust of Queen
   Elizabeth II   .15

1. *United States*, 50 Cents (S) 1936. Albany, New
   York Charter anniversary   50.00

BISON (BUFFALO)

Two hundred years ago, millions of bison wandered in herds over the North American prairies. As the settlers moved westward, these huge animals were so recklessly slaughtered that by 1890 only 1,000 of them were left. The specimen on which the U.S. coin was modelled weighed nearly a ton.

1. *United States*, 5 Cents (N) 1913–38. Indian head   .85

CAMEL

The dromedary or one-humped camel is one of the oldest domestic animals. Wild camels have all died out but they are still bred as pack animals and for riding. Riding a camel is like sitting on a seesaw. The camel picks up both legs on a side at the same time, pitching his passenger from side to side.

1. *Sudan*, 10 Piastres (CN) 1956– . Value (round
   planchet)   1.00
2. 5 Piastres (CN) 1956–   .60
3. 2 Piastres (CN) 1956–   .35
4. 10 Milliemes (Br) 1956– (scalloped planchet)   .25
*5. 5 Milliemes (Br) 1956–   .20
6. 2 Milliemes (Br) 1956–   .15
7. 1 Millieme (Br) 1956– (round planchet)   .10
8. 25 Piastres (CN) 1968. F.A.O. issue   5.00
   Coins struck in cooperation with the United Nations' Food and Agriculture Organization were sold at a premium over their face value, the profits going to the "Food for All" program.

CATTLE (BRAHMA BULL)

The outstanding characteristics of Brahma bulls are the large hump over the shoulders and the heavy fold of loose skin below the throat. Native to India, the Brahma strain has been imported into the U.S.

*1. *India*, 2 Annas (CN) 1950–55. Asoka pillar
   (square planchet)   .50

9

2. 1 Anna (CN) 1950–55 (scalloped planchet) .35
3. ¼ Anna (CN) 1950–55 (square planchet) .25

1. *India* (State of Indore), ¼ Anna (C) 1886–1902.
   Native inscription 1.25
*2. ¼ Anna (C) 1886–1902 .75

3. 1 Rupee (S) 1899–1901. Portrait of Maharajah
   Shivaji Rao 75.00

CATTLE (CALF)

Calves are the young of domestic cows.
One clause of the deed to the land on which
New Rochelle, N.Y. was settled required that
a fatted calf be offered each year to the original
owner, John Pell, and his descendants.

1. *United States*, 50 Cents (S) 1938. New Rochelle,
   New York 300th anniversary 65.00

CATTLE (COW)

Coins of the island of Guernsey feature, of
course, one of the famous Guernsey cows.
Fawn colored with white markings, the
Guernseys are heavier than other breeds and
noted for their rich, yellow milk.

1. *Guernsey*, 3 Pence (CN) 1956; (thicker planchet)
   1959–66. Arms (scalloped planchet) .75
*2. 10 New Pence (CN) 1968 (round planchet) .60

1. *Uganda*, 5 Shillings (CN) 1968. F.A.O. issue 2.50

CATTLE (HORNED)

This classification embraces many varieties
of animals, a full range of domesticated

mammals from Europe, Asia, Africa and North and South America.

*1. *Argentina*, 20 Cents (Al-Br) 1942–50. Head of Liberty .75
2. 10 Cents (Al-Br) 1942–50 .25
3. 5 Cents (Al-Br) 1942–50 .15

1. *The Gambia*, 2 Shillings (CN) 1966. Draped bust of Queen Elizabeth II 1.00

*1. *Guyana*, 1 Dollar (CN) 1970. Head of Cuffy (leader of 1763 slave revolt). F.A.O. issue 2.50

1. *Iceland*, 10 Kronur (S) 1930. Ancient king of Thule seated on throne 75.00
2. 10 Kronur (CN) 1967–   Value 2.00
3. 5 Kronur (CN) 1967– 1.00

*4. 2 Kronur (Al-Br) 1946; (N-Bra) 1958– 1.50
5. 1 Krona (Al-Br) 1946; (N-Bra) 1958– .85
6. 500 Kronur (G) 1961. Head of Jon Sigurdsson, birth year commemorative 65.00

*1. *Ireland*, 1 Shilling (S) 1928–42; (CN) 1951–68. Harp 1.00
2. 5 New Pence (CN) 1969– .25

1. *Madagascar*, 5 Francs (Al) 1953. Bust of Republic .75
*2. 2 Francs (Al) 1948 .45
3. 1 Franc (Al) 1948 .25

1. *Malagasy Republic*, 5 Francs (St) 1966. Native flower .90
2. 2 Francs (St) 1965 .40
*3. 1 Franc (St) 1965 .25

11

1. *New Caledonia*, 20 Francs (N) 1967. Head of Republic   1.50

1. *United States*, 50 Cents (S) 1935. Spanish Trail commemorative   250.00

1. *Uruguay*, 10 Pesos (Al-Br) 1965. Bust of Artigas. The steer is in the lower right quarter of the arms which appear on many different Uruguayan coins   .75

CATTLE (OXEN)

Oxen are known to have served man as docile workers since as far back in history as the Neolithic times. A pronounced hump on their backs distinguishes oxen from other cattle.

1. *Albania*, 5 Francs (S) 1925–27. Head of President Zogu   200.00

2. *United States*, 50 Cents (S) 1926–39. Oregon Trail Memorial   15.00

CATTLE (YAK)

Native to the plateau areas of Tibet and central Asia, yaks have been domesticated for more than 3,000 years. Usually black and white, yaks are known for their sure-footed climbing ability and their endurance in all kinds of weather.

*1. *Nepal*, 10 Paisa (Bra) 1967– . Mountains   .60
2. 5 Paisa (Al) 1967–   .40

COBRA

Deadly poisonous cobras live in Africa, Arabia, India, South China, Malaya and the Philippines, where certain species of these snakes grow to as much as 12 feet long.

* 1. *Thailand*, 10 Satangs (CN) 1908–37. Ornamental design (holed planchet) .50
  2. 5 Satangs (CN) 1908–37 (holed planchet) .35
  3. 1 Satang (Br) 1908–41 (holed planchet) .25

CROCODILE

Native to the tropical waters of Asia, Africa, Australia, and America, these aquatic reptiles have been known to attain a length of 20 feet. They are strong, vicious fighters with a long snout full of teeth.

1. *The Gambia*, 4 Shillings (CN) 1966. Bust of Queen Elizabeth II 2.50

DEER

Deer are predominantly woodland animals with species found in almost all parts of the world. The males or stags grow long, branched horns.

* 1. *China* (Formosa) 100 Yuan (S) 1965. Sun Yat-sen commemorative 3.50
  2. 50 Yuan (CN) 1965 1.75

1. *Mauritius*, ½ Rupee (S) 1934. Crowned head of King George V 4.00
2. ½ Rupee (S) 1938, 46; (CN) 1950, 51. Crowned head of King George VI 3.00
* 3. ½ Rupee (CN) 1965. Crowned head of Queen Elizabeth II 1.00

DOG

Domesticated centuries ago, dogs are known for their loyalty and protective instinct. The Irish Wolfhound and Norwegian Elkhound are pictured on their nation's coins.

1. *Bulgaria*, 10 Leva (CN) 1930. Value 2.00
* 2. 5 Leva (CN) 1930 1.00

13

1. *Ireland*, 6 Pence (N) 1928–41; (CN) 1942– . Harp .35

1. *Norway*, 50 Ore (CN) 1958. Head of King Olav V .50

ELEPHANT

The two types of elephants surviving today are the small Asiatic and the large African species. The ivory tusks of an African elephant weigh as much as 200 pounds and grow to a length of 10 feet. Elephants eat as much as a quarter of a ton of green foliage and drink 50 gallons of water a day.

1. *Belgian Congo*, 50 Francs (S) 1944. Value 30.00
2. 5 Francs (Bra) 1947, 48 5.00
*3. 2 Francs (Bra) 1943 (hexagonal planchet) 7.50
4. 2 Francs (Bra) 1946, 47 (round planchet) 1.25
5. 1 Franc (Bra) 1944–49 1.00

1. *German East Africa*, 15 Rupees (G) 1916. Heraldic eagle 125.00

1. *Israel*, 1 Pound (CN) 1961. Heroism and Sacrifice commemorative 5.00

1. *Ivory Coast*, 10 Francs (S) 1966. Head of President Boigny 10.00

*1. *Liberia*, 2 Cents (Bra) 1937; (CN) 1941. Palm tree .75
2. 1 Cent (Br) 1937; (CN) 1941 .50
3. ½ Cent (Br) 1937; (CN) 1941 .35
4. 5 Cents (CN) 1960– .25
5. 1 Cent (Br) 1960 .15

14

1. *Malawi*, 1 Florin (N) 1964. Head of Dr. Hastings
Banda — 1.50

1. *Rhodesia and Nyasaland*, 1 Penny (Br) 1955–63.
Value and ornaments (holed planchet) — .35

1. *Somalia*, 10 Cents (Br) 1950. Star and value — .65
2. 5 Cents (Br) 1950 — .45
3. 1 Cent (Br) 1950 — .25

1. *Thailand*, 1 Tical (S) 1908. Bust of King Chula-
longkorn in bemedalled uniform — 75.00

2. 20 Satangs (CN) 1897. Value — 12.50
3. 10 Satangs (CN) 1897 — 10.00
4. 5 Satangs (CN) 1897 — 7.50
5. 2½ Satangs (CN) 1897 — 8.50
6. 1 Tical (S) 1913–18. Bust of King Vajiravudh — 5.00
7. ½ Tical (S) 1915–21 — 2.50
8. ¼ Tical (S) 1915–25 — 1.50

* 9. ½ Tical (S) 1929. Bust of King Prajadhipok — 5.00
10. ¼ Tical (S) 1929 — 4.00

GAZELLE

Gazelles wander through eastern and northern Africa, central and western Asia and in
parts of India. Some species stand as high as
three feet at the shoulder and all are known for
their grace and speed.

* 1. *Qatar and Dubai*, 50 Dirhem (CN) 1966. Inscription and value — .75
2. 25 Dirhem (CN) 1966 — .45
3. 10 Dirhem (CN) 1966 — .30
4. 5 Dirhem (CN) 1966 — .20
5. 1 Dirhem (CN) 1966 — .15

GAZELLE (SPRINGBOK)

Springboks are found mainly in South
Africa. They are noted for their ability to leap
lightly and suddenly into the air.

15

open country in Africa where they travel at a gallop at more than 30 miles per hour.

1. *Rhodesia and Nyasaland*, ½ Penny (Br) 1955. Value (holed planchet)   .20

1. *South Africa*, 1 Sovereign (G) 1952. Head of King George VI   35.00
2. ½ Sovereign (G) 1952   22.50
3. 5 Shillings (S) 1947–52   5.00
4. 1 Sovereign (G) 1953–60. Head of Queen Elizabeth II   75.00
5. ½ Sovereign (G)   60.00
6. 5 Shillings (S) 1953–59   10.00
7. 2 Rand (G) 1961–64. Bust of Jan van Riebeeck   27.50
8. 1 Rand (G) 1961–64   17.50
*9. 50 Cents (S) 1961–64   6.50

HIPPOPOTAMUS

Living along the river banks of Africa, hippopotamuses feed at night on aquatic plants and, at times, on planted crops. One of the largest living mammals, an average hippopotamus weighs between 3 and 4 tons, stands almost 4 feet at the shoulder and can grow to be 14 feet long.

*10. 1 Rand (S) 1965–68. Profile portrait of Jan van Riebeeck, SOUTH AFRICA   3.00
11. 1 Rand (S) 1965–68. SUID AFRIKA   3.00
12. 1 Rand (S) 1967. Profile portrait of Hendrik Vorwoerd, SOUTH AFRICA   3.50
13. 1 Rand (S) 1967. SUID AFRIKA   3.50

GIRAFFE

Standing as high as 18 feet, giraffes are the tallest mammals. Very timid, giraffes live in

1. *The Gambia*, 8 Shillings (CN) 1970. Draped bust of Queen Elizabeth II   3.00

1. *Mali*, 5 Francs (A) 1961. Value   2.00

HORSE

Although very little is known about the origin of these animals, domesticated horses have been used for farming, hunting, warfare and racing since prehistoric times. The many species of horses shown on coins range from thoroughbred Lipizzaner stallions to wiry Mongolian ponies.

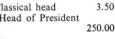

1. *Albania*, 1 Lek (N) 1926–31. Classical head   3.50
*2. 100 Franka Ari (G) 1926, 27. Head of President Zogu   250.00

1. *Argentina*, 10 Pesos (St) 1962– . Value (12-sided planchet)   .30

1. *Australia*, 1 Florin (S) 1935. Crowned head of King George V. Victoria and Melbourne centenary commemorative   50.00

1. *Austria*, 5 Schillings (S) 1960–67; (CN) 1968– Arms   .45

1. *British Caribbean Territories*, 50 Cents (CN) 1955. Crowned head of Queen Elizabeth II   2.50

1. *Bulgaria*, 10 Leva (CN) 1930. Value   2.00
*2. 5 Leva (CN) 1930   1.00

17

1. *Czechoslovakia*, 10 Koruny (S) 1968. Arms. National Theatre commemorative — 3.00

1. *Egypt*, 5 Pounds (G), 1955, 57. Winged sun and inscription — 250.00
2. 1 Pound (G) 1955, 57 — 50.00
*3. ½ Pound (G) 1958. United Arab Republic commemorative — 25.00

1. *Germany* (Prussia), 3 Marks (S) 1913. Eagle with snake. War of Liberation centenary commemorative — 6.00
*2. 2 Marks (S) 1913 — 3.00

3. 3 Marks (S) 1915. Heraldic eagle. Mansfield-Prussia centenary commemorative — 15.00

*1. *Great Britain*, 1 Sovereign (G) 1900–01. Veiled bust of Queen Victoria — 18.50
2. ½ Sovereign (G) 1900–01 — 13.50
3. 1 Crown (S) 1900 — 20.00
4. 1 Sovereign (G) 1902–10. Head of King Edward VII — 17.50
5. ½ Sovereign (G) 1902–10 — 13.50
6. 1 Crown (S) 1902 — 60.00
7. 5 Pounds (G) 1911. Head of King George V — 225.00
8. 2 Pounds (G) 1911 — 135.00
9. 1 Sovereign (G) 1911–25 — 17.50
10. ½ Sovereign (G) 1911–15 — 12.50
11. 5 Pounds (G) 1937. Head of King George VI — 375.00
12. 2 Pounds (G) 1937 — 225.00
13. 1 Sovereign (G) 1937 — 125.00
14. ½ Sovereign (G) 1937 — 60.00
15. 1 Crown (CN) 1951. Festival of Britain commemorative — 10.00

16. 1 Crown (S) 1935. Silver Jubilee commemorative — 12.50
17. 1 Crown (CN) 1953. Queen Elizabeth Coronation commemorative — 5.00

18

1. *Greece*, 20 Drachmai (S) 1960–65. Head of King
   Paul I   3.50

1. *India*, 1 Pice (Br) 1950. Asoka pillar   .15

1. *Ireland*, ½ Crown (S) 1928–42; (CN) 1951– . Harp   2.00

1. *Italy*, 5 Lire (S) 1914. Military bust of King
   Victor Emmanuel III   350.00
2. 2 Lire (S) 1908–17   2.50
3. 1 Lira (S) 1908–17   1.25
4. 10 Lire (S) 1926–34. Head of King Victor Emmanuel III   2.50

5. 20 Lire (S) 1936–41   100.00

6. 500 Lire (S) 1961. Seated figure of Italia. Unifica-
   tion centenary commemorative   4.00

 *1. *Lithuania*, 5 Litai (S) 1925. Value   20.00
  2. 2 Litu (S) 1925   8.50
  3. 1 Litas (S) 1925   6.00
  4. 50 Centu (Al-Br) 1925   5.00
  5. 20 Centu (Al-Br) 1925   3.50
  6. 10 Centu (Al-Br) 1925   3.00
  7. 5 Centai (Al-Br) 1925; (Br) 1936   2.50
  8. 2 Centai (Br) 1936   3.00
  9. 1 Centas (Al-Br) 1925; (Br) 1936   2.00
 10. 10 Litu (S) 1936. Head of Vytautas   25.00
 11. 5 Litai (S) 1936. Head of Dr. Basanivicius   10.00

19

1. *Luxembourg*, 100 Francs (S) 1946. Head of John the Blind (1310–46). Commemorative struck on 600th anniversary of his death ... 8.50
2. 50 Francs (S) 1946 ... 4.00
*3. 20 Francs (S) 1946 ... 2.00

1. *Mali*, 10 Francs (Al) 1961. Value ... 2.00

1. *Mexico*, 1 Peso (S) 1910–14. Eagle and serpent ... 12.50

1. *Monaco*, 100 Francs (CN) 1950. Head of Prince Rainier ... 2.50
*2. 50 Francs (Al-Br) 1950 ... 1.50

1. *Mongolia*, 20 Mung (N) 1945. Value in wreath ... 10.00
2. 15 Mung (N) 1945 ... 8.50
3. 10 Mung (N) 1945 ... 7.50
*4. 5 Mung (Al-Br) 1945 ... 8.50
5. 2 Mung (Al-Br) 1945 ... 6.50
6. 1 Mung (Al-Br) 1945 ... 7.50
7. 20 Mung (Al) 1959 ... 6.00
8. 15 Mung (Al) 1959 ... 4.50
9. 10 Mung (Al) 1959 ... 4.00

1. *Norway*, 1 Krone (CN) 1958. Head of King Olav V ... .85

*1. *Portugal*, 10 Escudos (S) 1928. Arms. Battle of Ourique (1139) commemorative ... 7.50

*1. *Spain*, 10 Centimos (Al) 1940–53. Eagle and arms ... .50
2. 5 Centimos (Al) 1940–53 ... .35

20

1. *Switzerland*, 5 Francs (S) 1939. Inscription. Zurich Exposition commemorative   8.50

*1. *Uruguay*, 1 Peso (S) 1917. Bust of Artigas   20.00
2. 50 Cents (S) 1916, 17   4.00
3. 20 Cents (S) 1920   2.50

1. *United States*, 1 Dollar (S) 1900. Conjoined heads of George Washington and Gen. Lafayette   150.00

1. *Vatican City*, 50 Lire (St) 1967. Bust of Pope Paul   .50

2. 50 Cents (S) 1925. Stone Mountain Memorial commemorative   12.50

3. 50 Cents (S) 1936. York County, Maine Tercentenary commemorative   25.00

1. *Venezuela*, 5 Bolivares (S) 1900–36. Head of Bolivar   6.00
The horse is in the lower half of the arms which appear on many different Venezuelan coins.

21

JAGUAR

Natives of South and Central America and some parts of Texas, jaguars feed on cattle, horses, tapir and dogs. They grow to 4 feet long. Living in forest areas, jaguars' orange-tan coats with rosette-shaped spots serve to blend the animals in with their surroundings.

*1. *Guyana*, 50 Cents (CN) 1967. Value .65
2. 25 Cents (CN) 1967 .40
3. 10 Cents (CN) 1967 .25

1. *Uruguay*, 10 Cents (Al-Br) 1930, 36. Head of Liberty 1.25
*2. 1 Peso (S) 1942. Head of Artigas 3.50

KANGAROO

Kangaroos are native to Australia where they travel in small herds or mobs. Standing as much as 8 feet tall, kangaroos range in color from gray to brown and red. They live on vegetation, preferring forested areas in which to live. Mother kangaroos carry their young in a protective front pouch.

*1. *Australia*, 1 Florin (S) 1910. Crowned bust of King Edward VII 10.00
2. 1 Shilling (S) 1910 5.00
3. 6 Pence (S) 1910 2.50
4. 3 Pence (S) 1910 1.50
5. 1 Florin (S) 1911–36. King George V 3.50
6. 1 Shilling (S) 1911–36 2.00
7. 6 Pence (S) 1911–36 1.00
8. 3 Pence (S) 1911–36 .65
9. 1 Florin (S) 1938–52. Head of King George VI 1.25
10. 6 Pence (S) 1938–52 .40
11. 1 Florin (S) 1953–63. Head of Queen Elizabeth II 1.00
12. 6 Pence (S) 1953–64 .35

13. 1 Penny (Br) 1938–52 .25
*14. 1 Penny (Br) 1953–64 .20
*15. ½ Penny (Br) 1939–52 .20
16. ½ Penny (Br) 1953–64 .15

17. 1 Florin (S) 1954. Royal Visit commemorative 4.00

18. 50 Cents (S) 1966. Draped bust of Queen Elizabeth II 2.00

LEOPARD

Bloodthirsty, ferocious members of the cat family, leopards inhabit Africa and Asia including Java, where they grow to a length of 6 to 7 feet. Equally at home in tropical forests or dry mountain areas, leopards can climb as well as spring after game.

1. *Congo*, 10 Sengi (Al) 1967. Value .75

LION

Found today mostly in Africa, Mesopotamia and northwestern India, lions like sandy, rocky areas and tall grass lands. They live on such animals as zebras, buffalo and antelope.

1. *Albania*, ½ Lek (N) 1926. Double-headed eagle 1.50
*2. ½ Lek (N) 1930, 31. Arms on shield 2.50

3. ¼ Lek (N) 1926, 27. Value 1.25
4. 5 Qindar Leku (Br) 1926 1.25

1. *Australia*, 1 Florin (S) 1954. Head of Queen Elizabeth II (same as Kangaroo #17) 3.00

1. *Belgian Congo*, 5 Francs (N-Br) 1936, 37. Head of King Leopold III 6.00

*1. *Belgium*, 5 Francs (N) 1938, 39. Shields 1.50
2. 1 Franc (N) 1939, 40 .75

1. *Congo* (Katanga Province), 10 Francs (Al) 1965. Value 1.00

23

*1. *Bulgaria*, 10 Leva (CN) 1930. Value   2.00
2. 5 Leva (CN) 1930   1.00

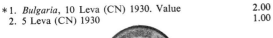

1. *Burundi*, 1 Franc (Bra) 1965. Value in circle   1.00

1. *Ethiopia*, 1 Talari (S) 1894–1904. Crowned head of
  Menelik II   20.00
2. ½ Talari (S) 1894–1925   4.50
3. ¼ Talari (S) 1894–1925   3.00
4. 1/16 Talari (S) 1894–1928   1.50
*5. 50 Cents (S) 1944. Bust of Emperor Haile
  Selassie I   3.50
6. 25 Cents (Br) 1944 (scalloped edge planchet)   .60
7. 10 Cents (Br) 1944 (round planchet)   .35
8. 5 Cents (Br) 1944   .20
9. 1 Cent (Br) 1944   .15

1. *East Africa* (as East Africa and Uganda Pro-
  tectorate), 50 Cents (S) 1906–10. Crowned bust of
  King Edward VII   6.00
2. 25 Cents (S) 1906–10   3.50
3. 50 Cents (S) 1911–19. Crowned bust of King
  George V   4.00
4. 25 Cents (S) 1911–18   3.00
*5. *East Africa* (administrative grouping of five
  territories), 1 Florin (S) 1920, 21   12.00
6. 1 Shilling (S) 1920, 21   15.00
7. 25 Cents (S) 1920, 21   7.50
8. 1 Shilling (S) 1921–25 (new standard)   3.00
9. 50 Cents—½ Shilling (S) 1921–24   2.25
10. 1 Shilling (S) 1937–46. Crowned head of King
  George VI   2.50
11. 50 Cents (CN) 1937–48   1.50
12. 50 Cents (CN) 1954–63. Crowned head of
  Queen Elizabeth II   .50

*1. *German East Africa*, 1 Rupee (S) 1890–1902.
  Helmeted bust of Kaiser Wilhelm   8.50
2. ½ Rupee (S) 1891–1901   4.50
3. ¼ Rupee (S) 1891–1901   3.00

1. *Great Britain*, 10 New Pence (CN) 1968. Draped
  bust of Queen Elizabeth II   .60

24

*1. *Italian Somaliland*, 10 Lire (S) 1925. Crowned
   bust of King Victor Emmanuel   35.00
 2. 5 Lire (S) 1925   22.50

1. *Mali*, 25 Francs (A) 1961. Value   6.00

1. *Rhodesia-Nyasaland*, 6 Pence (CN) 1955–63.
   Head of Queen Elizabeth II   .50

1. *Italy*, 50 Cents (N) 1919–35. Head of King Victor
   Emmanuel   .65
2. 20 Lire (S) 1928. Helmeted head of King Victor
   Emmanuel. In commemoration of 10th anniversary of end of World War I   20.00

1. *Singapore*, 1 Dollar (CN) 1967– . Value   2.00

*1. *Lebanon*, 1 Piastre (CN) 1925–36. Wreath and
    inscription (holed planchet)   .50
 2. ½ Piastre (CN) 1934–36 (holed planchet)   .30
 3. 2½ Piastres (Al-Br) 1940 (holed planchet)   .50
*4. 10 Piastres (Al) 1952. Cedar tree   .60
 5. 5 Piastres (Al-Br) 1955–61   .20

*1. *Somalia*, 1 Somalo (S) 1950. Value   3.00
 2. 50 Centesimi (S) 1950   2.50

25

1. *Tibet*, 5 Shokang (C) 1953. Inscriptions   7.50
2. 3 Shokang (C) 1946   6.00

LIZARD (COLLARED)

Found only in the dry districts of Australia, this lizard has a fold of skin with bone-like rods which stands up like a collar when it is frightened or disturbed. The collared lizard depends on its whip-like tail for defense.

1. *Australia*, 2 Cents (Br) 1966. Head of Queen Elizabeth II   .15

LIZARD (TUATARA)

This unique form of lizard has survived only because of its isolation. Found today only on a few off-shore islands of New Zealand, the greenish-brown tuataras grow to $2\frac{1}{2}$ feet long and have a life span of nearly 300 years.

1. *New Zealand*, 5 Cents (CN) 1967. Draped bust of Queen Elizabeth II   .30

LLAMA

Native to South America, llamas are domesticated beasts of burden with fine coats of wool. They are sure-footed, with great endurance, but refuse to move under a burden of more than 50 pounds.

*1. *Bolivia*, 50 Centavos (CN-St) 1965. Value. The llama appears in the arms on many Bolivian coins   .50
2. 20 Centavos (N-St) 1965   .25
3. 10 Centavos (C-St) 1965   .15
4. 5 Centavos (C-St) 1965   .10
5. 1 Peso (St) 1968. Value and inscription, F.A.O. "Food for All" commemorative   2.00

1. *Peru*, 1 Sol (Bra) 1943–65. Value. The llama is in the upper left quarter of the arms which appear on many Peruvian coins   .50
*2. $\frac{1}{2}$ Sol (Bra) 1935–65   .30
*3. 1 Sol (Bra) 1966– . Arms   .25
4. $\frac{1}{2}$ Sol (Bra) 1966–   .15

LYNX

Found in the northern areas of Europe and North America, the bewhiskered, sharp-eyed lynx prefer forestlands and rocky places. Their light brown, spotted skins have long been valuable in the fur trade.

1. *Canada*, 25 Cents (S) 1967. Draped bust of Queen Elizabeth II, commemorates the centennial of the Confederation .50

MOOSE

These large antlered mammals, known in America as moose and in Europe as elk, feed on birch and willow shoots and leaves. Shy, in spite of their size, moose frighten easily and gallop off at surprising speed.

* 1. *Norway*, 5 Ore (Br) 1958– . Head of King Olav V .20
* 1. *Canada,* 25 Cents (S) 1937–52. Head of King George VI .75
2. 25 Cents (S) 1953–64. Head of Queen Elizabeth II .50
3. 25 Cents (S) 1965, 66, 68; (N) 1968– . Draped bust of Queen Elizabeth II .50

MOUSE (FLYING)

Native to Australia, New Guinea and Tasmania, these shy, seldom-seen little animals have parachutelike folds of skin attached to their front legs, enabling them to make long sailing leaps.

1. *Australia*, 1 Cent (Br) 1966– . Draped bust of Queen Elizabeth II .10

PIG

Domesticated since about 3000 B.C., pigs are thought to be descendants of the wild boar of Europe. The animals on the Bermuda coin recall the wild hogs once there.

1. *Bermuda*, 1 Cent (Br) 1970. Draped bust of Queen Elizabeth II .15
1. *Ireland*, ½ Penny (Br) 1928–67. Harp .15

PLATYPUS

These unusual Australian mammals are equally at home on land or in the water. Platypuses have furry bodies, webbed feet, flat tails and soft, leathery ducklike beaks.

1. *Australia*, 20 Cents (S) 1966– Draped bust of Queen Elizabeth II .50

PUMA

One of the largest cats on the American continent, pumas grow to 40 inches long.

27

Also called catamounts, panthers or cougars, these cats rarely attack man.

1. *United States*, 50 Cents (S) 1927. Vermont Sesquicentennial commemorative   40.00

RABBIT

Rabbits and hares have been domesticated for centuries and are used for food in many countries as well as for their fur. These animals are distinguished by their powerful hind legs, long ears and fluffy tails.

1. *Canada*, 5 Cents (N) 1967. Draped bust of Queen Elizabeth II   .15

1. *Ireland*, 3 Pence (N) 1928–40; (CN) 1942– Harp   .25

1. *Tanzania*, 50 Cents (CN) 1966. Head of President Nyere   .40

SHEEP

The familiar Bible story of the Good Shepherd is referred to on the Vatican coins bearing sheep. These animals have long been kept for their flesh, skin and wool.

*1. *Australia*, 1 Shilling (S) 1938–52. Head of King George VI   1.00
2. 1 Shilling (S) 1953–63. Head of Queen Elizabeth II   .75

*1. *Cyprus*, 100 Mils (CN) 1963. Arms   1.25

1. *New Zealand*, ½ Crown (CN) 1953–65. Head of Queen Elizabeth II. The sheep as seen in the upper right quarter of the arms that appear on several New Zealand coins is taken from the Order of the Golden Fleece   1.50

*1. *Vatican City*, 2 Lire (N) 1929–37. Bust of Pope Pius XI   3.50
*2. 500 Lire (S) 1966. Head of Pope Paul VI wearing mitre   3.50

3. 100 Lire (St) 1966   1.50
4. 50 Lire (St) 1966   .75
5. 20 Lire (Al-Br) 1966   .35
6. 10 Lire (Al) 1966   .25
7. 5 Lire (Al) 1966   .20
8. 2 Lire (Al) 1966   .15
9. 1 Lira (Al) 1966   .10

SQUIRREL

Species of squirrel are found in most forested parts of the world. Distinguished by their long bushy tails, squirrels live in trees where they feed on nuts and fruits.

1. *Norway*, 1 Ore (Br) 1958– . Monogram   .10

TIGER

These big cats are found from Persia to Manchuria. Their stripes help the animals blend into the landscape of the grassy plains and swampland in which they live. Feeding on any mammal they can catch, tigers generally travel alone.

1. *India*, 1 Rupee (N) 1947. Crowned head of King
George VI   2.55
2. ½ Rupee (N) 1946, 47   1.25
3. ¼ Rupee (N) 1946, 47   1.00

WOLF

Wolves prey particularly on flocks of sheep and catch other animals by running them down. Often travelling in packs, wolves by their combined efforts are able to overpower large deer. The timber wolves of Canada have appeared in many adventure stories of the north.

1. *Canada*, 50 Cents (S) 1967. Draped bust of Queen
Elizabeth II   1.00

ZEBRA

The only striped members of the horse family, zebras inhabit Angola, the mountainous regions of South Africa and parts of Ethiopia, East Africa, and Uganda. Many species of zebra are already extinct and, since they are the favorite prey of lions, others are rapidly approaching extinction.

1. *Botswana*, 50 Cents (S) 1966. Head of Seretse
Kahma   5.00

Fish and Sea Animals

ANGELFISH

Found in tropical and sub-tropical waters, angelfish are flat, brilliantly colored fish. Several different species of tropical fish are popularly called angelfish because of their wing-like pectoral fins.

1. *Bermuda*, 5 Cents (CN) 1970– . Draped bust of Queen Elizabeth II .15

BONGA FISH

Found off the west coast of Africa, bonga fish are of the herring family and, fresh or dried, are an important source of food for the natives. They are distinguished by their deep forked tail.

1. *Sierra Leone*, ½ Cent (Br) 1964. Head of Sir Milton Margai .25

BONEFISH

Bonefish are fast-swimming, spirited members of the mackerel family. Living mostly in the warmer seas where they swim in large schools, bonefish have metallic blue backs with silver undersides.

1. *Bahamas*, 10 Cents (CN) 1966– . Draped bust of Queen Elizabeth II .30

CODFISH

Native to the North Atlantic and North Pacific oceans, cod are especially numerous off Newfoundland and Alaska. One of the most important fishes, they have olive tops with whitish grey undersides and speckles.

1. *Danzig*, 10 Pfennigs (Al-Br) 1932. Value 2.50

30

* *Indicates coin or coins illustrated*

DOLPHIN

The warm-blooded, air-breathing dolphin has figured in myths and fables from early times. Noted for their playful antics around ships at sea, dolphins are now being carefully studied since, of all the world's creatures, they alone have intelligence comparable to man's.

1. *Denmark*, 25 Ore (S) 1874–1905. Head of King
   Christian IX — 1.50
2. 10 Ore (S) 1874–1905 — .75
3. 5 Ore (Br) 1874–1906. Crowned monogram — .35
4. 2 Ore (Br) 1874–1906 — .25
5. 1 Ore (Br) 1874–1904 — .20
6. 2 Kroner (S) 1915, 16. Head of King Christian X — 4.50
*7. 1 Krone (S) 1915, 16 — 2.00

1. *Greece*, 20 Drachmai (S) 1960–65. Head of King
   Paul I — 3.50

1. *Italy*, 5 Lire (Al) 1951– . Boat rudder — .25

1. *United States*, 1 Dollar (G) 1915. Workman,
   Panama Pacific Exposition commemorative — 75.00

FLOUNDER

Flounders have an unusual flattened body well suited to life at the bottom of seas. Soon after the larvae are hatched, one of the eyes gradually moves to the other side of the head.

1. *Danzig*, 5 Pfennigs (Al-Br) 1932. Value — 1.25

LATIMERIA CHALUMNAE (COMORO FISH)

This species of fish was thought to have been extinct for 65 million years until 1938 when one was brought up alive in some fishermen's nets. A second specimen was caught in 1952 off of the Comoro Islands which have placed its likeness on their coins.

*1. *Comoro Islands*, 20 Francs (N-Bra) 1964. Bust of
   Liberty — 1.00
2. 10 Francs (N-Bra) 1964 — .60

LIONFISH

Native to the Indian Ocean, East Indies and Polynesia, the lionfishes' intricate pattern of light and dark blue stripes enables them effectively to camouflage themselves.

1. *Singapore*, 50 Cents (CN) 1967. Value   1.00

MACKEREL

A most important food fish, mackerel are characterized by streamlined, nearly scaleless bodies and deeply forked tails. The common Atlantic mackerels average about $1\frac{1}{2}$ pounds per fish, yet the annual commercial catch is some 50 million pounds.

1. *Canada*, 10 Cents (S) 1967. Draped bust of Queen Elizabeth II   .25

MARLIN

Blue marlin are deep sea, fighting game fish. They may reach as much as 1,000 pounds.

1. *Bahamas*, 50 Cents (S) 1966. Draped bust of Queen Elizabeth II   1.25

MUSSEL

Edible bivalves, mussels form large, crowded beds. In certain areas of Africa, New Guinea and Oceania the shells are used for barter and for making jewelry and buttons.

1. *New Hebrides*, 20 Francs (N) 1967. Head of
   Republic   1.50
∗2. 10 Francs (N) 1967   1.00

SAILFISH

Named for their high, wide dorsal fins, sailfish may reach a length of 10 feet and are prized both for game and as food. Like marlin, sailfish have a spearlike upper jaw.

1. *Tanzania*, 5 Senti (Br) 1966. Head of President
   Nyere   .20

SALMON

Although they spend their lives in the cold, deep waters of the oceans, salmon return to their fresh water hatching sites to spawn.

1. *Ireland*, 1 Florin (S) 1928–43; (CN) 1951–68.
   Harp 1.50
*2. 10 New Pence (CN) 1969 .... .35

SEAHORSE

Both mythical and real sea horses appear on coins. Actual sea horses are small fish that live in warm seas. They swim in an upright position by rapidly beating their fins. At rest, they wrap their tail around a piece of seaweed.

*1. *Greece*, 2 Drachmai (S) 1911. Head of King
   George I 4.50
2. 1 Drachma (S) 1910, 11 .... 3.00

1. *Singapore*, 10 Cents (CN) 1967. Value ..... .35

SHELL FISH (CONCH)

Known for their heavy, spiral shells, conchs are found on the sandy bottoms of shallow tropical waters. Some species are edible and their shells are used for cameos, buttons and as horns.

1. *Bahamas*, 1 Dollar (S) 1966. Draped bust of
   Queen Elizabeth II 2.50

1. *India* (Travancore), 1 Chuckram (Br) 1939–45.
   Bust of Maharajah Bala Rama Varma. The
   conch shell design appears on many coins of this
   native state 1.50

STARFISH

The largest of the starfish or sea stars found off the Bahamas grow to 20 inches in diameter. The body of the starfish is a central disk from which a number of arms (usually five) radiate.

33

1. *Bahamas*, 1 Cent (Bra) 1966. Draped bust of Queen Elizabeth II .10

SWORDFISH

Swordfish are great game fish and much appreciated as food. They are named for their long, broad, sharp upper jaw which they use to flail smaller fish.

1. *Singapore*, 20 Cents (CN) 1967. Value .50

TRITON

Native to tropical waters, the Pacific triton's shells are still used as horns by the natives of the area. Some of the 120 species of triton contain a meat-eating snail.

*1. *Comoro Islands*, 20 Francs (N-Bra) 1964. Bust of Liberty 1.00
2. 10 Francs (N-Bra) 1964 .60

TURTLE

The largest turtles in the world are found in the South Pacific. Some reach 6 feet in length and weigh nearly 1,000 pounds. Their bodies are enclosed in shells covered with horny plates and they have strong, toothless jaws with sharp cutting edges.

1. *Fiji Islands*, 6 Pence (S) 1934–36. Crowned head of King George V 2.50
2. 6 Pence (S) 1937–43. Crowned head of King George VI 1.00
*3. 6 Pence (CN) 1953–67. Crowned head of Queen Elizabeth II .35

1. *Tonga*, 2 Seniti (Br) 1967. Head of Queen Salote .35
*2. 1 Seniti (Br) 1967 .25
3. 2 Seniti (Br) 1968. King Taufa'ahau Tupou IV .30
4. 1 Seniti (Br) 1968 .20

WHALE

Although they stay underwater for up to half an hour, whales breathe air and must surface to expel air from a blow hole in the top of their heads.

1. *United States*, ½ Dollar (S) 1935. Hudson, N.Y. sesquicentennial commemorative 250.00

Birds and Insects

BEE

More than 800,000 different insects have been noted. Among these are honey bees which live in well-ordered, disciplined colonies with a queen, drones and workers. Some colonies have as many as 90,000 bees. Bees have often been used as symbol of industrious workers and savers.

1. *Italy*, 10 Cents (Br) 1919–37. Head of King Victor Emmanuel   .25

2. 2 Lire (Al) 1953–59. Olive branch   .15

1. *Norway*, 10 Ore (CN) 1958– Monogram   .25

CHICKEN

The most common of all poultry species, chickens are descended from the jungle fowl of India. Since ancient times, chickens have represented fertility.

*1. *Ajman*, 5 Rials (S) 1970. Value   5.00
2. 2 Rials (S) 1970   2.50
3. 1 Rial (S) 1970   1.75

1. *Ireland*, 1 Penny (Br) 1928–68. Harp   .20

* *Indicates coin or coins illustrated*

COCK (ROOSTER)

Cocks or roosters are the male of the common barnyard fowl. Cocks also symbolize pugnacity and were used as a badge by the Free French Forces during World War II.

*1. *Cameroun*, 1 Franc (Al-Br) 1943. Cross of
   Lorraine   2.50
  2. 50 Cents (Al-Br) 1943   1.75

  1. *French Equatorial Africa*, 1 Franc (Bra) 1942.
    Cross of Lorraine   2.50
*2. 50 Centimes (Bra) 1942   2.00

  1. *Madagascar*, 1 Franc (Br) 1943. Cross of Lor-
    raine   4.00
  2. 50 Centimes (Br) 1943   2.50

*1. *France*, 20 Francs (G) 1901–14. Head of Liberty   20.00
  2. 10 Francs (G) 1901–14   15.00

  3. 50 Francs (Al-Br) 1950–58   .60
*4. 20 Francs (Al-Br) 1950–58   .40
  5. 10 Francs (Al-Br) 1950–59   .25

1. *Malawi*, 6 Pence (N) 1964. Head of Dr. Hastings
   Banda   .60

CONDOR

Found only in the high Andes mountains, these South American vultures are about 4 feet long with a wing spread of 9 feet. Condors have been known to attack animals as large as deer. These birds can fly to a height of 23,000 feet.

1. *Bolivia*, 50 Centavos (St) 1965. Value. The condor is above the coat-of-arms that appears on many coins of Bolivia   .35

*1. *Chile*, 1 Peso (S) 1910–32; (CN) 1933–40. Value   .75
  2. 20 Centavos (S) 1899–1920; (CN) 1920–41   .40
  3. 10 Centavos (S) 1899–1920; (CN) 1920–41   .25
  4. 5 Centavos (S) 1899–1919; (CN) 1920–38   .20
*5. 10 Pesos (Al) 1956. Value   .60
  6. 5 Pesos (Al) 1956   .45

7. 10 Centesimos (Al-Br) 1960– . Value .30
8. 5 Centesimos (Al-Br) 1960– .25
9. 2 Centesimos (Al-Br) 1964– .15
10. 1 Centesimo (Al) 1960– .10
11. ½ Centesimo (Al) 1962– .10

1. *Colombia*, 50 Centavos (CN) 1958– . Head of
Bolivar. The condor is above the coat-of-arms
which appears on many Colombian coins .50

1. *Ecuador*, 1 Sucre (N-St) 1964– . Head of Gen.
Sucre. The condor is above the coat-of-arms
which appears on many Ecuadorian coins .50

CRANE

Cranes are considered a symbol of good
luck and long life. They have a rich, compact
plumage with a partly bald head.

. *South Africa*, 5 Cents (N) 1965–69. Head of Jan
van Riebeeck, SOUTH AFRICA .25
. 5 Cents (N) 1965–69. SUID AFRIKA .25

3. 5 Cents (N) 1968. Head of Charles Swart, SOUTH
AFRICA .25
4. 5 Cents (N) 1968. SUID AFRIKA .25

1. *Turks & Caicos*, 1 Crown (CN) 1969. Draped bust
of Queen Elizabeth II 2.50

*1. *Uganda*, 2 Shillings (CN) 1966. Arms .75
2. 1 Shilling (CN) 1966 .45
3. 50 Cents (CN) 1966 .30

4. 1 Crown (CN) 1968. F.A.O. "Food for All" issue 2.50

37

EAGLE

Eagles were used on coins as symbols of power as long ago as 300 B.C. They were carried on the standards of the Roman legions and Napoleon's armies. The American bald (white-headed) eagle became the national emblem of the U.S. in 1782.

1. *Germany* (Prussia), 3 Marks (S) 1913. King on horseback, War of Liberation commemorative   6.00
* 2.   2 Marks (S) 1913   3.50

1. *Germany* (Republic), 5 Marks (S) 1930. Eagle and shield, Evacuation of the Rhineland commemorative   20.00
* 2.   3 Marks (S) 1930   10.00

1. *Albania*, 2 Francs (S) 1926–28. Sower   17.50

2.   10 Qindar Lek (Br) 1926. Value   3.50

1. *Mexico*, 1 Peso (S) 1957– . Bust of Morelos. The eagle badge of Mexico appears on one side of all the nation's coins   .50

* 1. *Austria*, 100 Kronen (Br) 1923, 24. Value   .50
2.   1 Groschen (Br) 1925–38   .25

1. *Biafra*, 1 Shilling (Al) 1969. Native design   1.00

1. *Rhodesia*, 2 Shillings—20 cents (CN) 1964. Draped bust of Queen Elizabeth II   2.00

1. *Rhodesia and Nyasaland*, ½ Crown (CN) 1955–57.
   Head of Queen Elizabeth II   2.00
2. 2 Shillings (CN) 1955–57   1.25

6. 20 Dollars (G) 1907–33. Facing figure of Liberty   70.00

*1. *United States*, 20 Dollars (G) 1850–1907. Liberty
    head   60.00
2. 10 Dollars (G) 1838–1907   30.00
3. 5 Dollars (G) 1839–1908   25.00
4. 2½ Dollars (G) 1840–1907. Liberty coronet   35.00

*7. 10 Dollars (G) 1907–33. Liberty in Indian war
    bonnet   60.00
*8. 5 Dollars (G) 1908–1929. Indian head (incuse
    design)   25.00
9. 2½ Dollars (G) 1908–1929 (incuse design)   25.00

5. 1 Dollar (S) 1878–1921. Liberty head   2.50

10. 1 Dollar (S) 1921–35. Head of Liberty with
    radiant crown   2.50

39

11. 50 Cents (S) 1916–47. Walking figure of Liberty   1.00
12. 25 Cents (S) 1916–30. Standing figure of Liberty   2.50

16. 50 Cents (S) 1935. Connecticut Tercentenary commemorative   50.00

13. 50 Cents (S) 1915. Panama Pacific Exposition commemorative   85.00

17. 50 Cents (S) 1946. Iowa Centennial commemorative   20.00

14. 50 Cents (S) 1921. Alabama Centennial commemorative   60.00

18. 50 Cents (S) 1918. Illinois Centennial commemorative   25.00

15. 50 Cents (S) 1935. Arkansas Centennial commemorative   15.00

19. 50 Cents (S) 1925. Stone Mountain Memorial   12.50

20. 50 Cents (S) 1934–8. Texas Centennial   15.00

21. 2½ Dollars (G) 1915. Panama-Pacific Exposition commemorative   350.00

1. *Zambia*, 5 Shillings (N) 1964. President Kaunda   3.50

in small herds in open grassland, eat herbs, fruits, berries, roots and insects.

1. *Australia*, 1 Florin (S) 1910. Crowned head of King Edward VII   10.00
*2. 1 Shilling (S) 1910   5.00
3. 6 Pence (S) 1910   2.50
4. 3 Pence (S) 1910   1.50
5. 1 Florin (S) 1911–36. Crowned head of King George V   3.50
6. 1 Shilling (S) 1911–36   2.00
7. 6 Pence (S) 1911–36   1.00
8. 3 Pence (S) 1911–36   .65

*9. 1 Florin (S) 1938–52. Head of King George VI   1.25
10. 6 Pence (S) 1938–52   .40
11. 1 Florin (S) 1953–63. Head of Queen Elizabeth II   1.00
12. 6 Pence (S) 1953–63   .40

2. *Zambia*, 2 Ngwee (Br) 1968. Head of President Kuanda   .30

EMU

Large, flightless birds, emus are native to the Australian area. They grow to be nearly 6 feet tall and are very fast runners. Emus live

*13. 50 Cents (S) 1966. Draped bust of Queen Elizabeth II   2.00
14. 50 Cents (CN) 1969–   . (12-sided planchet)   1.50

FLAMINGO

Found in tropical and subtropical areas, flamingos are wading birds with pink or red feathers. They have very long legs and necks, webbed feet and a broad bill that bends abruptly downwards.

1. *Bahamas*, 2 Dollars (S) 1966. Draped bust of Queen Elizabeth II   5.00

GOOSE

Canada geese are known for their honking call and the V formation in which they fly. They have black feathers on their head and neck, white on their throat and body.

1. *Canada*, 1 Dollar (S) 1967. Draped bust of Queen Elizabeth II   1.75

GROUSE

Native to the colder parts of the Northern Hemisphere, grouse are game birds with mottled plumage which enables them to conceal themselves in their surroundings.

1. *Norway*, 2 Ore (Br) 1958– . Monogram   .15

HERON

Poor walkers, herons are graceful in the air and fly with their necks folded back on their shoulders. They are known throughout the world.

1. *Singapore*, 5 Cents (CN) 1967– . Value   .25

HORNBILL

Native to Africa and Asia, hornbills are noted for their large down-curved bills capped by a horny, helmet-like growth.

1. *Zambia*, 1 Shilling (CN) 1964– . Arms   .85
2. 1 Shilling (CN) 1966. Head of President Kaunda   .65
*3. 10 Ngwee (CNZ) 1968   .65

LONG TAIL (BIRD OF SPRING)

These beautiful birds are noted for their ability to soar and float in the air. Rodents robbing their nests have driven the birds to gather high on the Bermuda cliffs for protection.

1. *Bermuda*, 25 Cents (CN) 1970. Draped bust of Queen Elizabeth II   .50

LYRE BIRD

Singing a fine song and proudly showing off their 16 beautiful tail feathers in the form of an ancient lyre, the male birds go courting. Native to the bushlands and rugged mountain areas of Australia, these birds are great mimics and fast walkers but do not like to fly.

1. *Australia*, 10 Cents (CN) 1966– . Draped bust of Queen Elizabeth II   .30

NEW CALEDONIA NATIVE BIRD

Facing extinction, these timid birds are found only in the thickest mountain forest areas of New Caledonia. They form their own family (Rhinochetidae).

*1. *New Caledonia*, 5 Francs (Al) 1952. Seated female figure   .75
2. 2 Francs (Al) 1949   .40
3. 1 Franc (Al) 1949   .25
4. 50 Centimes (Al) 1949   .15

NEW ZEALAND HUIA BIRD

These beautiful birds were native only to a small mountainous region of New Zealand and are now extinct. The long, attractive tail feathers of the huia were highly prized by native Maori chiefs who wore them as an insignia of their rank.

1. *New Zealand*, 6 Pence (S) 1933–36. Crowned head of King George V   .85
2. 6 Pence (S) 1937–46; (CN) 1947–52. Head of King George VI   .75
*3. 6 Pence (CN) 1953–65. Head of Queen Elizabeth II   .50

NEW ZEALAND KIWI BIRD

This shy, flightless bush bird got its name from its characteristic cry of "k—wee." Having poor eyesight, the kiwi has developed an acute sense of smell and is a swift runner. Kiwis are about the size of a large chicken but their rudimentary wings are only 2 inches long. Female kiwis lay eggs that weigh about one pound, a quarter of their own weight.

1. *New Zealand*, 1 Florin (S) 1933–36. Crowned
   head of King George V   2.75
2. 1 Florin (S) 1937–46; (CN) 1947–51. Head of
   King George VI   1.00
*3. 1 Florin (CN) 1953–65. Head of Queen Elizabeth
   II   1.00

4. 20 Cents (CN) 1967– . Draped bust of Queen
   Elizabeth II   .60

NEW ZEALAND TUI BIRD

These beautiful songbirds are native only to the forest areas of New Zealand. Also called parson-birds, tui have black plumage in green metallic shades, shimmering violet shoulders with white tufts of feathers at the throat. Noted for their ability to mimic other birds and sounds, tui are now in danger of extinction.

1. *New Zealand*, 1 Penny (Br) 1940–52. Head of
   King George VI   .35
*2. 1 Penny (Br) 1953–65. Head of Queen Elizabeth II   .30

OSPREY

Noisy, singing ospreys are known all over the world. Large birds with wing spreads of up to 6 feet, ospreys feed only on live fish, plunging feet first into the water to grasp their prey.

1. *Finland*, 10 Markkaa (S) 1967. 50th year of In-
   dependence commemorative   4.50

OSTRICH

The largest of living birds, ostrich live in troupes of 10–15 each, growing to a height of 8 feet. Ostrich weigh as much as 300 pounds.

1. *Tanzania*, 20 Senti (N-Br) 1966. Head of President
   Nyere   .30

OWL

Disks of radiating feathers around their eyes give these birds a studious look. In mythology, owls are related to Athena (Minerva), goddess of wisdom.

*1. *Greece*, 10 Lepta (CN) 1912. Inscription (holed
   planchet)   .45
2. 5 Lepta (CN) 1912 (holed planchet)   .40

1. *Sweden*, 5 Kronor (S) 1962. Head of King Gustaf
   VI Adolf   6.00

1. *United States*, 50 Dollars (G) 1915. Head of Minerva, Panama-Pacific Exposition commemorative (round planchet)   6000.00

2. 50 Dollars (G) 1915 (octagonal planchet)   4500.00

PARTRIDGE

Partridges have been esteemed as game birds for years. They have a variegated plumage for concealment.

1. *The Gambia*, 3 Pence (N-Bra) 1966. Draped bust
   of Queen Elizabeth II   .25

45

PHEASANT

Male pheasants are vain and beautiful birds noted for their long tails. Their feathers are brown, blue, black, green and gold.

1. *Nepal*, 2 Paisa (Al) 1966. Mountains   .30

PIGEON (DOVE)

The names pigeon and dove are used interchangeably and, for centuries, these birds have been looked upon as symbols of peace and gentleness.

1. *Canada*, 1 Cent (Br) 1967. Draped bust of Queen Elizabeth II, Confederation centennial commemorative   .10

1. *Czechoslovakia*, 25 Koruny (S) 1965. Arms, 20th anniversary of Czech liberation commemorative   6.00

1. *Denmark*, 2 Kroner (S) 1903. Bust of King Christian IX, 40th year of reign commemorative   7.50

1. *Hungary*, 10 Filler (Al-Br) 1946–50. Value   .25

1. *Japan*, 5 Sen (T) 1945, 46. Value   .35

2. 5 Yen (Bra) 1948, 49. Building   .35

3. 1 Sen (Br) 1938; (Al) 1938–40, smaller planchet. Inscription   .30

1. *Rumania*, 100,000 Lei (S) 1946. Head of King Mihai I   30.00

1. *Switzerland*, 5 Francs (S) 1936. Inscription, Armament Fund issue   15.00

*1. *Vatican City*, 10 Lire (S) 1939. Arms of Cardinal Pacelli (Sede Vacante issue)   7.50
 2. 5 Lire (S) 1939   5.00

*3. 10 Centesimi (Bra) 1942–46. Bust of Pope Pius XII   .50
 4. 5 Centesimi (Bra) 1942–46   .75

5. 2 Lire (Al) 1950 (Holy Year issue)   1.50

6. 500 Lire (S) 1958. Arms (Sede Vacante issue)   10.00

*7. 20 Lire (Al-Br) 1962. Bust of Pope John XXIII   1.00
 8. 10 Lire (Al) 1962   .85
 9. 5 Lire (Al) 1962   .65
10. 2 Lire (Al) 1962. Arms   .45
11. 1 Lira (Al) 1962   .25

12. 500 Lire (S) 1963. Arms of Cardinal Masella. (Sede Vacante issue)   5.00

47

QUETZAL

Small birds with brilliant green and red feathers, quetzals have long, golden green tail plumes that reach a length of $3\frac{1}{2}$ feet. The tail feathers were worn as headdresses by the Mayan priests and nobles.

1. *Guatemala*, 50 Centavos (Bra) 1962, 63. White Nun Orchid. The Quetzal is in the coat-of-arms that appears on most Guatemalan coins ... 2.50

2. 25 Centavos (S) 1943. Government building ... 3.00

SPARROW

Known all over the world, the small dull colored sparrows are valuable to farmers because they eat weed seeds.

1. *South Africa*, ¼ Penny (Br) 1923–31. Crowned head of King George V ... 2.50
2. ¼ Penny (Br) 1937–52. Head of King George VI ... .25
3. ¼ Penny (Br) 1953–60. Head of Queen Elizabeth II ... .10
*4. ¼ Cent (Bra) 1961–64. Bust of Jan van Riebeeck ... .10

5. 1 Cent (Br) 1965–69, SOUTH AFRICA ... .10
6. 1 Cent (Br) 1965–69, SUID AFRIKA ... .10
*7. 1 Cent (Br) 1968. Bust of Charles Swart, SOUTH AFRICA ... .10
8. 1 Cent (Br) 1968, SUID AFRIKA ... .10

TITMOUSE

The cheerful little red-brown, white and black titmice destroy harmful grubs and insects.

1. *Norway*, 25 Ore (CN) 1958– . Head of King Olav V ... .35

WOODCOCK

Also called snipes, woodcock are shy, nocturnal feeders.

1. *Ireland*, 1 Farthing (Br) 1928–66. Harp ... .20

WREN

Almost all members of the large and varied wren family are untiring singers.

1. *Great Britain*, 1 Farthing (Br) 1937–52. Head of King George VI ... .20
*2. 1 Farthing (Br) 1953–56. Head of Queen Elizabeth II ... .35